Picture Books In Winter

Summer fading, winter comes–
   Frosty mornings, tingling thumbs,
Window robins, winter nooks,
   And the picture storybooks.

Water now is turned to stone
   Nurse and I can walk upon;
Still we find the flowing brooks
   In the picture storybooks.

All the pretty things put by,
   Wait upon the children's eye,
Sheep and shepherds, trees and crooks,
   In the picture storybooks.

We may see how all things are,
   Seas and cities, near and far,
And the flying fairies' looks,
   In the picture story books.

How am I to sing your praise,
   Happy chimney-corner days,
Sitting safe in nursery nooks,
   Reading picture storybooks?

ROBERT LOUIS STEVENSON

About Patricia Ludlow

Apart from one short spell in her life when she liked the idea of being a vet, Patricia Ludlow had her heart set on becoming an artist at the early age of three years. Subsequently, she attended her hometown Rochdale School of Art and then went on to study at St. Martin's and Camberwell art schools in London.

She was first employed as a sculptress, before working for a Mayfair publisher and then becoming a full-time illustrator. Since then, Patricia has produced illustrations for numerous magazines, book jackets and many books for children.

Patricia has no children and lives near Rochdale with her two cats, Lupin (a Siamese) and Jaffa Cake (a ginger-and-white). Her hobbies (when she has time) are collecting antiques and tending her garden.

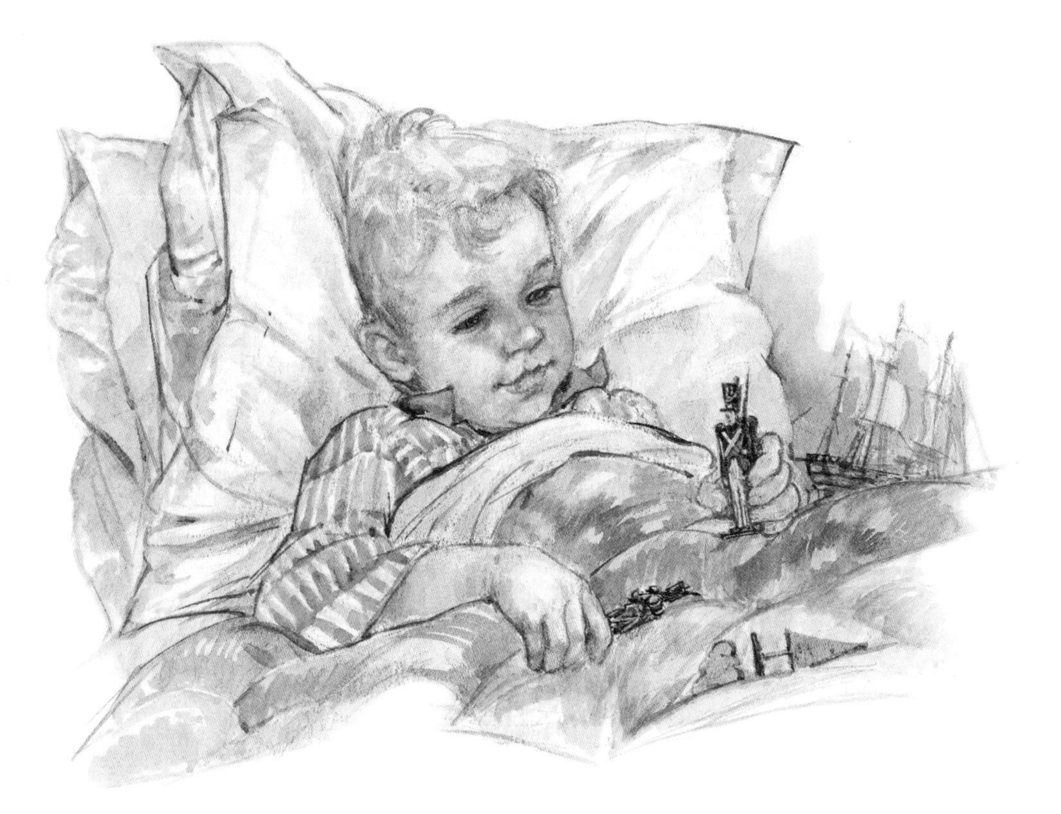

First published 1999 by Kibworth Books
Imperial Road, Kibworth Beauchamp, Leics. LE8 0HR
Reprinted 2000

ISBN: 0-7239-0193-7
Printed in Singapore

The Children's TREASURY of VERSE

Compiled and
designed by Desmond Marwood

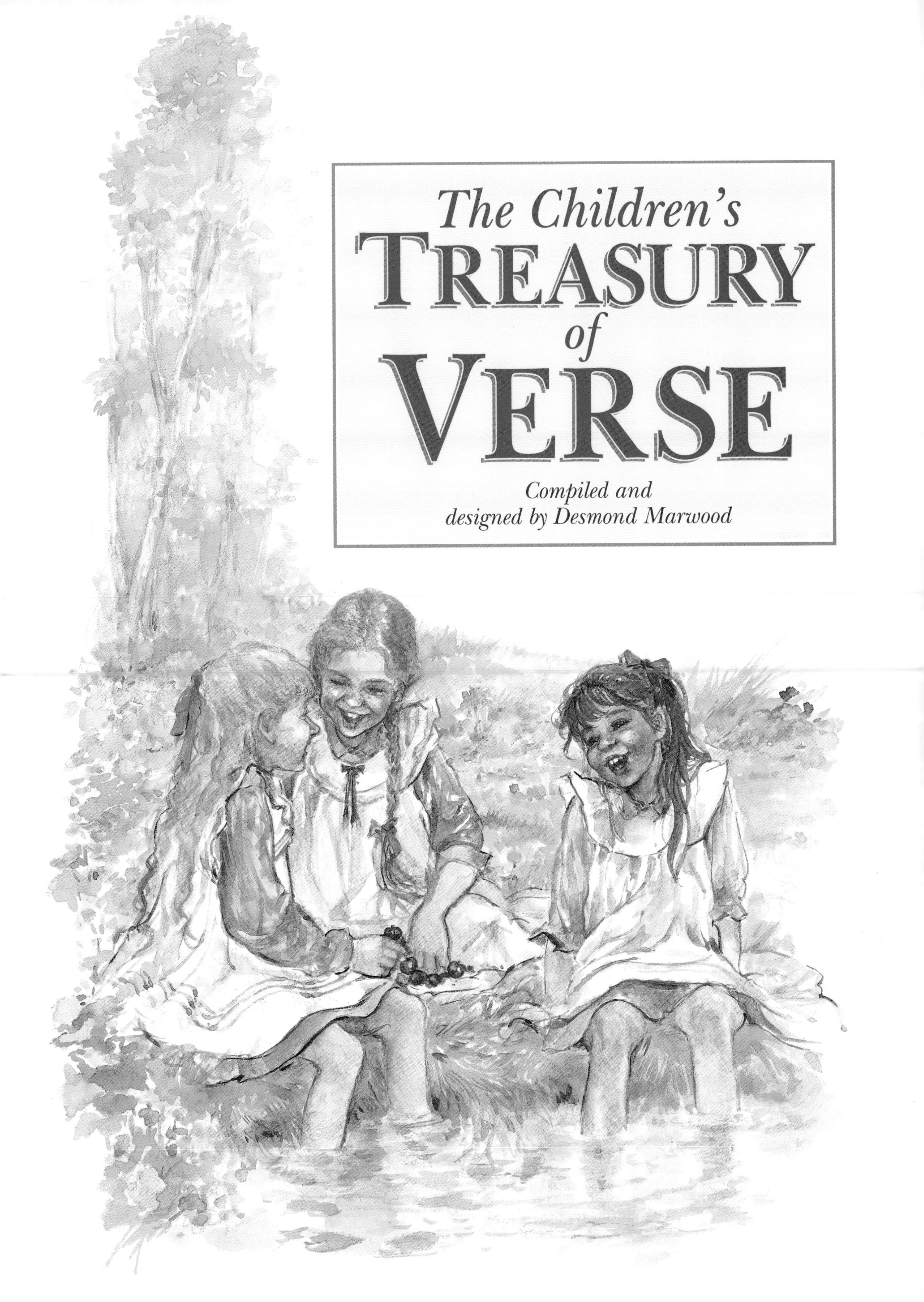

CHILDHOOD DAYS

Whole Duty of Children

A child should always say what's true,
  And speak when he is spoken to,
And behave mannerly at table:
  At least as far as he is able.

ROBERT LOUIS STEVENSON

My Shadow

I have a little shadow that goes in and out with me,
And what can be the use of him is more than I can see.
He is very, very like me from the heels up to the head;
And I see him jump before me when I jump into my bed.

The funniest thing about him is the way he likes to grow –
Not at all like proper children, which is always very slow;
For he sometimes shoots up taller, like an india-rubber ball,
And he sometimes gets so little that there's none of him at all.

He hasn't got a notion of how children ought to play,
And can only make a fool of me in every sort of way.
He stays so close behind me he's a coward you can see;
I'd think shame to stick to nursie as that shadow sticks to me!

One morning, very early, before the sun was up,
I rose and found the shining dew on every buttercup;
But my lazy little shadow, like an arrant sleepy-head,
Had stayed at home behind me and was fast asleep in bed.

ROBERT LOUIS STEVENSON

Playgrounds

In summer I am glad
  We children are so small,
For we can see a thousand things
  That men can't see at all.

They don't know much about the moss
  And all the stones they pass;
They never lie and play among
  The forests in the grass.

They walk about a long way off
  And, when we're at the sea,
Let father stoop as best he can,
  He can't find things like me.

But when the snow is on the ground,
  And all the puddles freeze,
I wish that I were very tall,
  High up above the trees.

LAURENCE ALMA-TADEMA

Grammar in Rhyme

Three little words you often see
  Are *Articles* A, An, and The.
A *Noun* is the name of anything,
  As School or Garden, Hoop or Swing.
Adjectives tell the kind of Noun,
  As Great, Small, Pretty, White or Brown.
In front of *Nouns,* the *Pronouns* stand:
  Her head, His face, Your arm, My hand.
Verbs tell of something being done:
  To Read, Count, Laugh, Sing, Jump or Run.
How things are done, the *Adverbs* tell,
  As Slowly, Quickly, Ill or Well.
Conjunctions join the words together,
  As men And women, wind And weather.
The *Preposition* stands before
  A *Noun,* as In or Through a door.
The *Interjection* shows surprise,
  As Oh! how pretty! Ah! how wise!
The whole are called nine parts of speech,
  Which reading, writing, speaking teach.

ANONYMOUS

The Swing

How do you like to go up in a swing,
Up in the air so blue?
Oh, I do think it the pleasantest thing
Ever a child can do!

Up in the air and over the wall,
Till I can see so wide,
Rivers and trees and cattle and all
Over the countryside –

Till I look down on the garden green,
Down on the roof so brown –
Up in the air I go flying again,
Up in the air and down!

ROBERT LOUIS STEVENSON

Mister Nobody

I know a funny little man,
As quiet as a mouse,
Who does the mischief that is done
In everybody's house!
There's no one ever sees his face,
And yet we all agree
That every plate we break was cracked
By Mister Nobody.

'Tis he who always tears our books,
Who leaves the door ajar,
He pulls the buttons from our shirts,
And scatters pins afar;
That squeaking door will always squeak
For, prithee don't you see,
We leave the oiling to be done
By Mister Nobody.

He puts damp wood upon the fire,
That kettles cannot boil;
His are the feet that bring in mud,
And all the carpets soil.
The papers always are mislaid,
Who had them last but he?
There's no one tosses them about
But Mister Nobody.

The finger marks upon the door
By none of us are made;
We never leave the blinds unclosed
To let the curtains fade;
The ink we never spill; the boots
That lying round you see
Are not our boots – they all belong
To Mister Nobody.

ANONYMOUS

Boy's Song

Where the pools are bright and deep,
Where the grey trout lies asleep,
Up the river and over the lea,
That's the way for Billy and me.

Where the blackbird sings the latest,
Where the hawthorn blooms the sweetest,
Where the nestlings chirp and flee,
That's the way for Billy and me.

Where the mowers mow the cleanest,
Where the hay lies thick and greenest,
There to track the homeward bee,
That's the way for Billy and me.

Where the hazel bank is steepest,
Where the shadow falls the deepest,
Where the clustering nuts fall free,
That's the way for Billy and me.

Why the boys should drive away
Little sweet maidens from the play,
Or love to banter and fight so well,
That's the thing I could never tell.

But this I know, I love to play
Through the meadow, among the hay;
Up the water and o'er the lea,
That's the way for Billy and me.

JAMES HOGG

Marching Song

Bring the comb and play upon it!
Marching, here we come!
Willie cocks his highland bonnet,
Johnnie beats the drum.

Mary Jane commands the party,
Peter leads the rear;
Feet in time, alert and hearty,
Each a Grenadier!

All in the most martial manner
Marching double quick;
While the napkin like a banner
Waves upon the stick!

ROBERT LOUIS STEVENSON

A Birthday Thought

I live once more to see the day
That brought me first to light;
Oh! teach my willing heart the way
To take Thy mercies right!

Though dazzling splendour, pomp and show
My fortune has denied,
Yet more than grandeur can bestow
Content hath well supplied.

I envy no one's birth or fame,
Their titles, train, or dress,
Nor has my pride e'er stretched its aim
Beyond what I possess.

I ask and wish not to appear
More beauteous, rich, or gay;
Please, make me wiser every year,
And better every day.

ANONYMOUS

Past, Present, Future

Tell me, tell me, smiling child,
What the past is like to thee?
"An Autumn evening soft and mild
With a wind that sighs mournfully."

Tell me, what is the present hour?
"A green and flowery spray
Where a young bird sits gathering its power
To mount and fly away."

And what is the future, happy one?
"A sea beneath a cloudless sun;
A mighty, glorious, dazzling sea
Stretching into infinity."

EMILY BRONTË

Jemima

There was a little girl, she wore a little hood,
And a curl down the middle of her forehead,
When she was good, she was very, very good,
But when she was bad, she was horrid.

One day she went upstairs, while her parents, unawares,
In the kitchen down below were occupied with meals,
And she stood upon her head, on her little truckle-bed,
And she then began hurraying with her heels.

Her mother heard the noise, and thought it was the boys,
A-playing at a combat in the attic,
But when she climbed the stair and saw Jemima there,
She rebuked her naughty daughter most emphatic!

ANONYMOUS

Another Plum-Cake

"Oh! I've got a plum-cake, and a feast let us make;
Come, schoolfellows, come at my call;
I assure you 'tis nice, and we'll each have a slice,
Here's more than enough for us all."

Thus said little Jack, as he gave it a smack,
And sharpen'd his knife to begin;
Nor was there one found, upon the play-ground,
So cross that he would not come in.

With masterly strength, he cut through it at length,
And gave to each playmate a share:
Charles, William, and James, and many more names,
Partook his benevolent care.

And when it was done, and they'd finished their fun,
To marbles or hoop they went back;
And each little boy felt it always a joy,
To do a good turn for good Jack.

In his task and his book, his best pleasures he took,
And as he thus wisely began,
Since he's been a man grown he has constantly shown
That a good boy will make a good man.

ANN and JANE TAYLOR

Monday's Child

Monday's child is fair of face,
 Tuesday's child is full of grace,
Wednesday's child is full of woe,
 Thursday's child has far to go,
Friday's child is loving and giving,
 Saturday's child works hard for its living,
And a child that's born on the Sabbath day
 Is fair and wise and good at play.

ANONYMOUS

A Good Play

We built a ship upon the stairs
 All made of the back-bedroom chairs,
And filled it full of sofa pillows
 To go a-sailing on the billows.

We took a saw and several nails,
 And water in the nursery pails;
And Tom said, "Let us also take
 An apple and a slice of cake,"
Which was enough for Tom and me
 To go a-sailing on, till tea.

We sailed along for days and days,
 And had the very best of plays;
But Tom fell out and hurt his knee,
 So there was no one left but me.

ROBERT LOUIS STEVENSON

WEIRD and WONDERFUL

Flower in a Crannied Wall

Flower in the crannied wall,
   I pluck you out of the crannies,
I hold you here, root and all, in my hand,
   Little flower - but if I could understand
What you are, root and all, and all in all,
   I should know what God and man is.

ALFRED, LORD TENNYSON

I Wandered Lonely As A Cloud

I wandered lonely as a cloud
That floats on high o'er vales and hills,
When all at once I saw a crowd,
A host, of golden daffodils;
Beside the lake, beneath the trees,
Fluttering and dancing in the breeze.

Continuous as the stars that shine
And twinkle on the Milky Way,
They stretched in never-ending line
Along the margin of a bay:
Ten thousand saw I at a glance,
Tossing their heads in sprightly dance.

The waves beside them danced, but they
Out-did the sparkling waves in glee:
A poet could not but be gay,
In such jocund company:
I gazed – and gazed – but little thought
What wealth the show to me had brought:

For oft, when on my couch I lie,
In vacant or in pensive mood,
They flash upon that inward eye
Which is the bliss of solitude;
And then my heart with pleasure fills,
And dances with the daffodils.

WILLIAM WORDSWORTH

Topsy-Turvy World

If the butterfly courted the bee,
And the owl the porcupine;
If churches were built in the sea,
And three times one was nine;
If the pony rode his master,
If the buttercups ate the cows,
If the cat had the dire disaster,
To be worried, sir, by the mouse;
If mamma, sir, sold the baby
To a gipsy for half-a-crown;
If a gentleman, sir, was a lady,
The world would be Upside-Down!
If any of all these wonders
Should ever come about
I should not consider them blunders,
For I should be Inside-Out!

Baa baa, black wool,
Have you any sheep?
Yes, sir, a packfull,
Creep, mouse, creep!
Four-and-twenty little maids
Hanging out the pie,
Out jumped the honey-pot,
Guy Fawkes, Guy!
Cross latch, cross latch,
Sit and spin the fire,
When the pie was opened,
The bird was on the brier!

WILLIAM BRIGHTY RANDS

The Fairy Folk

Come, cuddle close in Daddy's coat
Beside the fire so bright,
And hear about the fairy folk
That wander in the night.
For when the stars are shining clear
And all the world is still
They float across the silver moon
From hill to cloudy hill.

Their caps of red, their cloaks of green,
Are hung with silver bells,
And when they're shaken in the wind
Their merry ringing swells.
And, riding on the crimson moth
With black spots on their wings,
They guide them down the purple sky
With golden bridle rings.

They love to visit girls and boys
To see how sweet they sleep,
To stand beside their cosy cots
And at their faces peep.
For in the whole of fairyland
They have no finer sight
Than little children sleeping sound
With faces rosy bright.

On tip-toe crowding round their heads
When bright the moonlight beams,
They whisper little tender words
That fill their minds with dreams;
And when they see a sunny smile,
With lightest finger tips,
They lay a hundred kisses sweet
Upon the ruddy lips.

And then the little spotted moths
Spread out their crimson wings,
And bear away the fairy crowd
With shaking bridle rings.
Come, bairnies, hide in Daddy's coat
Beside the fire so bright –
Perhaps the little folk
Will visit you tonight.

ROBERT BIRD

The World

Great, wide, beautiful, wonderful world,
With the wonderful water around you curled,
And the wonderful grass upon your breast –
World, you are beautifully dressed,

The wonderful air is over me,
And the wonderful wind is shaking the tree,
It walks on the water and whirls the mills,
And talks to itself on the tops of the hills.

You friendly Earth! How far you go,
With the wheat fields that nod and the rivers that flow,
With cities and gardens, and cliffs and isles,
And people upon you for thousands of miles!

Ah! You are so great and I am so small
I tremble to think of you, World, at all.
And yet when I said my prayers today
A whisper inside me seemed to say:
"You are more than the Earth, though you are such a dot;
You can love and think, and the Earth cannot!"

WILLIAM BRIGHTY RANDS

The Fairies

Up the airy mountain,
  Down the rushy glen,
We daren't go a-hunting
  For fear of little men;
Wee folk, good folk,
  Trooping all together;
Green jacket, red cap,
  And white owl's feather!

Down along the rocky shore,
  Some make their home,
They live on crispy pancakes
  Of yellow tide-foam;
Some in the reeds
  Of the black mountain lake,
With frogs for their watchdogs,
  All night awake.

High on the hill-top
  The old King sits;
He is now so old and grey
  He's nigh lost his wits.
With a bridge of white mist
  Columbkill he crosses,
On his stately journeys
  From Slieveleague to Rosses.

Or going up with music
  On cold, starry nights,
To sup with the Queen
  Of the gay Northern Lights.
They stole little Bridget
  For seven years long;
When she came down again
  Her friends were all gone.

They took her lightly back,
Between the night and morrow,
They thought that she was fast asleep,
But she was dead with sorrow.
They have kept her ever since
Deep within the lake,
On a bed of flag-leaves,
Watching till she wake.

By the craggy hillside,
Through the mosses bare,
They have planted thorn trees
For pleasure here and there.
Is any man so daring
As dig them up in spite,
He shall find their sharpest thorns
In his bed at night.

Up the airy mountain,
Down the rushy glen,
We daren't go a-hunting
For fear of little men;
Wee folk, good folk,
Trooping all together;
Green jacket, red cap,
And white owl's feather!

WILLIAM ALLINGHAM

The Butterfly's Ball

Come, take up your hats, and away let
us haste
To the Butterfly's Ball and the
Grasshopper's Feast;
The trumpeter Gadfly has summoned
the crew,
And the revels are now only waiting
for you.

On the smooth-shaven grass by the
side of the wood,
Beneath a broad oak that for ages has
stood,
See the children of earth and the tenants
of air
For an evening's amusement together
repair.

And there came the Beetle, so blind
and so black,
Who carried the Emmet, his friend, on
his back;
And there was the Gnat, and the Dragon-
fly too,
With all their relations, green, orange,
and blue.

And there came the Moth in his plumage
of down,
And the Hornet in jacket of yellow and
brown,
Who with him the Wasp, his companion
did bring,
But they promised that evening to lay by
their sting.

And the shy little Dormouse crept out
of his hole,
And led to the feast his blind brother,
the Mole;
And the Snail, with his horns peeping
out of his shell,
Came from a great distance – the length
of an ell.

A mushroom their table, and on it was
laid
A water dock leaf, which a table-cloth
made;
The viands were various, to each of
their taste,
And the Bee brought his honey to
crown the repast.

There close on his haunches, so solemn
and wise,
The Frog from a corner looked up to
the skies;
And the Squirrel, well pleased such
diversion to see,
Sat cracking his nuts overhead in
a tree.

Then out came the Spider, with fingers
so fine,
To show his dexterity on the
tight line:
From one branch to another his cobwebs
he slung,
Then as quick as an arrow, he
darted along.

But just in the middle, oh! shocking
to tell!
From his rope in an instant, poor
Harlequin fell;
Yet he touched not the ground, but
with talons outspread,
Hung suspended in air at the end of
a thread.

Then the Grasshopper came with a
jerk and a spring,
Very long was his leg, though but
short was his wing;
He took but three leaps, and was soon
out of sight,
Then chirped his own praises the rest
of the night.

With step so majestic the Snail did
advance,
And promised the gazers a minuet
to dance;
But they all laughed so loud that he
pulled in his head,
And went in his own little chamber
to bed.

Then as evening gave way to shadows
of night,
The watchman, the Glow-worm, came
out with his light;
Then home let us hasten while yet we
can see,
For no watchman is waiting for you
and for me.

WILLIAM ROSCOE

The Table and the Chair

Said the Table to the Chair,
  "You can hardly be aware
How I suffer from the heat
  And from chilblains on my feet.
If we took a little walk,
  We might have a little talk;
Pray let us take the air,"
  Said the Table to the Chair.

Said the Chair unto the Table,
  "Now you know we are not able:
How foolishly you talk,
  When you know we cannot walk!"
Said the Table with a sigh,
  "It can do no harm to try.
I've as many legs as you;
  Why can't we walk on two?"

So they both went slowly down,
  And walked about the town
With a cheerful bumpy sound
  As they toddled round and round;
And everybody cried,
  As they hastened to their side,
"See, the Table and the Chair
  Have come out to take the air!"

But in going down an alley
  To a castle in the valley,
They completely lost their way.
  And they wandered all the day
Till, to see them safely back,
  They paid a Ducky-quack,
And Beetle and a Mouse,
  Who took them to their house.

Then they whispered to each other,
  "Oh, delightful little brother,
What a lovely walk we've taken!
  Let us dine on beans and bacon."
So, the Ducky and the leetle
  Browny-Mousy and the Beetle
Dined and danced upon their heads
  Till they toddled to their beds.

EDWARD LEAR

The Fountain

Into the sunshine,
  Full of the light,
Leaping and flashing
  From morn till night!

Into the moonlight,
  Whiter than snow,
Waving so flower-like
  When the winds blow!

Into the starlight,
  Rushing in spray,
Happy at midnight,
  Happy by day!

Ever in motion,
  Blithesome and cheery,
Still climbing heavenward,
  Never aweary:

Glad of all weathers,
  Still seeming best,
Upward or downward,
  Motion thy rest;

Full of a nature
  Nothing can tame,
Changed every moment,
  Ever the same;

Ceaseless aspiring,
  Ceaseless content,
Darkness or sunshine
  Thy element;

Glorious fountain!
  Let my heart be
Fresh, changeful, constant,
  Upward like thee!

JAMES RUSSELL LOWELL

The Fairy Life

Where the bee sucks, there suck I;
In a cowslip's bell I lie;
There I couch when owls do cry.
On the bat's back I do fly
After summer merrily.
Merrily, merrily shall I live now
Under the blossom that hangs on the bough.

WILLIAM SHAKESPEARE

GREAT and SMALL

Hurt No Living Thing

Hurt no living thing;
  Ladybird, nor butterfly,
Nor moth with dusty wing,
  Nor cricket chirping cheerily,
Nor grasshopper so light of leap.
  Nor dancing gnat, nor beetle fat,
Nor harmless worms that creep.

CHRISTINA ROSSETTI

The Owl and the Pussycat

The Owl and the Pussycat went to sea
In a beautiful pea-green boat,
They took some honey and plenty of money,
Wrapped in a five-pound note.
The Owl looked up to the stars above,
And sang to a small guitar,
"O lovely Pussy! O Pussy, my love,
What a beautiful Pussy you are,
You are,
You are!
What a beautiful Pussy you are!"

Pussy said to the Owl, "You elegant fowl!
How charmingly sweet you sing!
Oh, let us be married! Too long have we tarried:
But what shall we do for a ring?"
They sailed away, for a year and a day,
To the land where the Bong-tree grows,
And there in a wood a Piggy-wig stood,
With a ring at the end of his nose,
His nose,
His nose,
With a ring at the end of his nose.

"Dear Pig, are you willing to sell for one shilling
Your ring?" Said the Piggy, "I will."
So they took it away, and were married next day
By the Turkey who lives on the hill.
They dined on mince and slices of quince,
Which they ate with a runcible spoon;
And hand in hand, on the edge of the sand,
They danced by the light of the moon,
The moon,
The moon,
They danced by the light of the moon.

EDWARD LEAR

The Robin

When up aloft
  I fly and fly,
I see in pools
  The shining sky,
And a happy bird
  Am I, am I!

When I descend
  Toward the brink
I stand and look
  And stop and drink
And bathe my wings,
  And chink and prink.

When winter frost
  Makes earth as steel,
I search and search
  But find no meal,
And most unhappy
  Then I feel.

But when it lasts,
  And snows still fall,
I get to feel
  No grief at all,
For I turn to a cold, stiff
  Feather ball!

THOMAS HARDY

Dobbin's Friend

Dobbin has a little friend,
Spotted white and sable;
Every day she goes to him
In his lonely stable.

Not a mite of dread has she,
Not a thought of danger;
Lightly runs between his hoofs,
Jumps upon his manger;

Lays her soft, warm cheek to his,
Purrs her meek: "Good morning!"
Gives the flies that hover near
Such a look of warning!

"Dobbin dear," she sometimes says,
"Feel my winter mittens!
Nice and warm, you see, and made
Purposely for kittens.

"Dobbin dear, such times at home!
Mother has caught a rat!
Brought it home to show us.
What do you think of that?

"Dobbin," she whispers, purring still,
"You often get so weary!
Why don't you balk or run away,
And get your freedom, dearie?"

Then Dobbin gives his head a toss,
And says: "For shame, Miss Kitty!
If I could do such a mean thing
'Twould be a monstrous pity!

"No, no, my master's good and kind!
I'll never vex him – never!"
And Kitty, pleased, still rubs his cheek,
And likes him more than ever.

MARY MAPES DODGE

The White Sea-Gull

The white sea-gull, the wild sea-gull!
 A joyful bird is he,
As he lies like a cradled thing at rest
 In the arms of the sunny sea!

The little waves wash to and fro,
 And the little white gull lies asleep;
As the fisher's boat with breeze and tide,
 Goes merrily over the deep.

The ship, with her sails set, goes by;
 And her people stand to note
How the sea-gull sits on the rocking waves,
 As still as an anchored boat.

The sea is fresh and the sea is fair,
 And the sky calm overhead;
And the sea-gull lies on the deep, deep sea,
 Like a king in his royal bed!

MARY HOWITT

What Would You Do?

Oh, what would you do if you had a cow
  Who never said: "Moo!" but preferred: "Bow-wow!";
Who played the guitar and lived in a sty,
  And put on goloshes to keep her feet dry!

ANONYMOUS

Time to Rise

A birdie with a yellow bill
  Hopped upon the window sill,
Cocked his shining eye and said:
  "Ain't you shamed, you sleepy head?"

ROBERT LOUIS STEVENSON

The Eagle

He clasps the crag with crooked hands;
  Close to the sun in lonely lands,
Ringed with the azure world he stands.

The wrinkled sea beneath him crawls;
  He watches from his mountain walls,
And like a thunderbolt he falls.

ALFRED, LORD TENNYSON

If You Should Meet a Crocodile

If you should meet a crocodile,
  Don't take a stick and poke him;
Ignore the welcome in his smile,
  Be careful not to stroke him.

For as he sleeps upon the Nile,
  He thinner gets and thinner;
And whene'er you meet a crocodile
  He's ready for his dinner.

ANONYMOUS

The Owl

When cats run home and light has come,
And dew is cold upon the ground,
And the far-off stream is dumb,
And the whirring sails go round,
And the whirring sails go round;
Alone and warming his five wits,
The white owl in the belfry sits.

When merry milkmaids click the latch,
And rarely smells the new-mown hay,
And the cock hath sung beneath the thatch
Twice or thrice his roundelay,
Twice or thrice his roundelay;
Alone and warming his five wits,
The white owl in the belfry sits.

ALFRED, LORD TENNYSON

The Perfect Greyhound

If you would have a good tyke,
Of which there are few like –
He must be headed like a snake,
Necked like a drake,
Backed like a bream,
Sided like a bream,
Tailed like a bat,
And footed like a cat.

ANONYMOUS

The Tiger

Tiger, Tiger, burning bright
In the forests of the night,
What immortal hand or eye
Could frame thy fearful symmetry?

In what distant deeps or skies
Burnt the fire of thine eyes?
On what wings dare he aspire?
What the hand dare seize the fire?

And what shoulder and what art
Could twist the sinews of thy heart?
And, when thy heart began to beat,
What dread hand forged thy dread feet?

What the hammer, what the chain,
In what furnace was thy brain?
What the anvil? What dread grasp
Dare its deadly terrors clasp?

When the stars threw down their spears,
And watered heaven with their tears,
Did He smile His work to see?
Did He who made the lamb make thee?

Tiger! Tiger! burning bright
In the forests of the night,
What immortal hand or eye
Dare frame thy fearful symmetry?

WILLIAM BLAKE

The Kitten and the Leaves

See the kitten on the wall,
  Sporting with the leaves that fall,
Withered leaves – one, two, and three –
  From the lofty elder tree!
Through the calm and frosty air
  Of this morning bright and fair,
Eddying round and round, they sink
  Softly, slowly: one might think,
From the motions that are made,
  Every little leaf conveyed
Sylph or fairy hither tending,
  To this lower world descending,
Each invisible and mute
  In his wavering parachute.
But the kitten, how she starts,
  Crouches, stretches, paws and darts,
First at one, and then its fellow,
  Just as light and just as yellow;
There are many now – now one –
  Now they stop and there are none:
What intenseness of desire
  In her upward eye of fire!
With a tiger-leap halfway
  Now she meets the coming prey,
Let it go as fast, and then
  Has it in her power again:
How she works with three or four,
  Like and Indian conjuror:
Quick as he in feats of art,
  Far beyond his joy of heart.
Were her antics played in the eye
  Of a thousand standers-by
Clapping hands with shouts and stare,
  What would little Tabby care
For the plaudits of the crowd?
  Over happy to be proud,
Over wealthy in the treasure
  Of her own exceeding pleasure!

WILLIAM WORDSWORTH

City Mouse and Garden Mouse

The city mouse lives in a house,
The garden mouse lives in a bower;
He's friendly with the frogs and toads,
And sees pretty plants in flower.

The city mouse eats bread and cheese,
The garden mouse eats what he can;
We will not grudge him seeds and stocks,
Poor little timid, furry man.

CHRISTINA ROSSETTI

To a Butterfly

I've watched you now a full half-hour,
Self-poised upon that yellow flower;
And, little butterfly, indeed
I know not if you sleep or feed.
How motionless! Not frozen seas
More motionless! And then
What joy awaits you when the breeze
Hath found you out among the trees,
And calls you forth again!

This plot of orchard ground is ours:
My trees they are, my sister's flowers.
Here rest your wings when they are weary,
Here lodge as in a sanctuary!
Come often to us, fear no wrong;
Sit near us on the bough!
We'll talk of sunshine and of song,
And summer days when we were young;
Sweet childish days that were as long
As twenty days are now.

WILLIAM WORDSWORTH

BEDTIME and DREAMS

How Many Miles to Babylon?

How many miles to Babylon?
  Three score miles and ten.
Can I get there by candlelight?
  Yes, and back again.
If your heels are nimble and light,
  You may get there by candlelight.

ANONYMOUS

The Shut-Eye Train

Come, my little one, with me!
There are wondrous sights to see
As the evening shadows fall,
In your pretty cap and gown.
Don't detain
The Shut-Eye Train –
"Ting-a-ling!" the bell it goeth,
"Toot-toot!" the whistle bloweth,
And we hear the warning call:
"All aboard for Shut-Eye Town!"

Over hill and over plain
Soon will speed the Shut-Eye train!
Through the blue where bloom the stars,
And the Mother Moon looks down,
We'll away
To land of Fay.
Oh, the sights that we shall see there!
Come, my little one, with me there –
'Tis a goodly train of cars –
All aboard for Shut-Eye Town.

Swifter than the wild bird's flight,
Through the realms of fleecy night
We shall speed and speed away!
Let the night with envy frown –
What care we
How wroth she be!
To the Balow-land above us,
To the Balow-folk who love us,
Let us hasten while we may –
All aboard for Shut-Eye Town!

Shut-Eye Town is passing fair,
Golden dreams await us there;
We shall dream those dreams, my dear,
Till the Mother Moon goes down –
See unfold
Delights untold!
And in those mysterious places
We shall see beloved faces,
And beloved voices hear
In the grace of Shut-Eye Town.

Heavy are our eyes my sweet,
Weary are our little feet –
Nestle closer up to me
In your pretty cap and gown;
Don't detain
The Shut-Eye Train!
"Ting-a-ling!" the bell it goeth,
"Toot-toot!" the whistle bloweth,
Oh, the sights that we shall see!
All aboard for Shut-Eye Town!

EUGENE FIELD

Bed in Summer

In winter I get up at night
And dress by yellow candle-light,
In summer, quite the other way,
I have to go to bed by day.

I have to go to bed and see
The birds still hopping on the tree,
Or hear the grown-up people's feet
Still going past me in the street.

And does it not seem hard to you,
When all the sky is clear and blue,
And I should like so much to play,
To have to go to bed by day?

ROBERT LOUIS STEVENSON

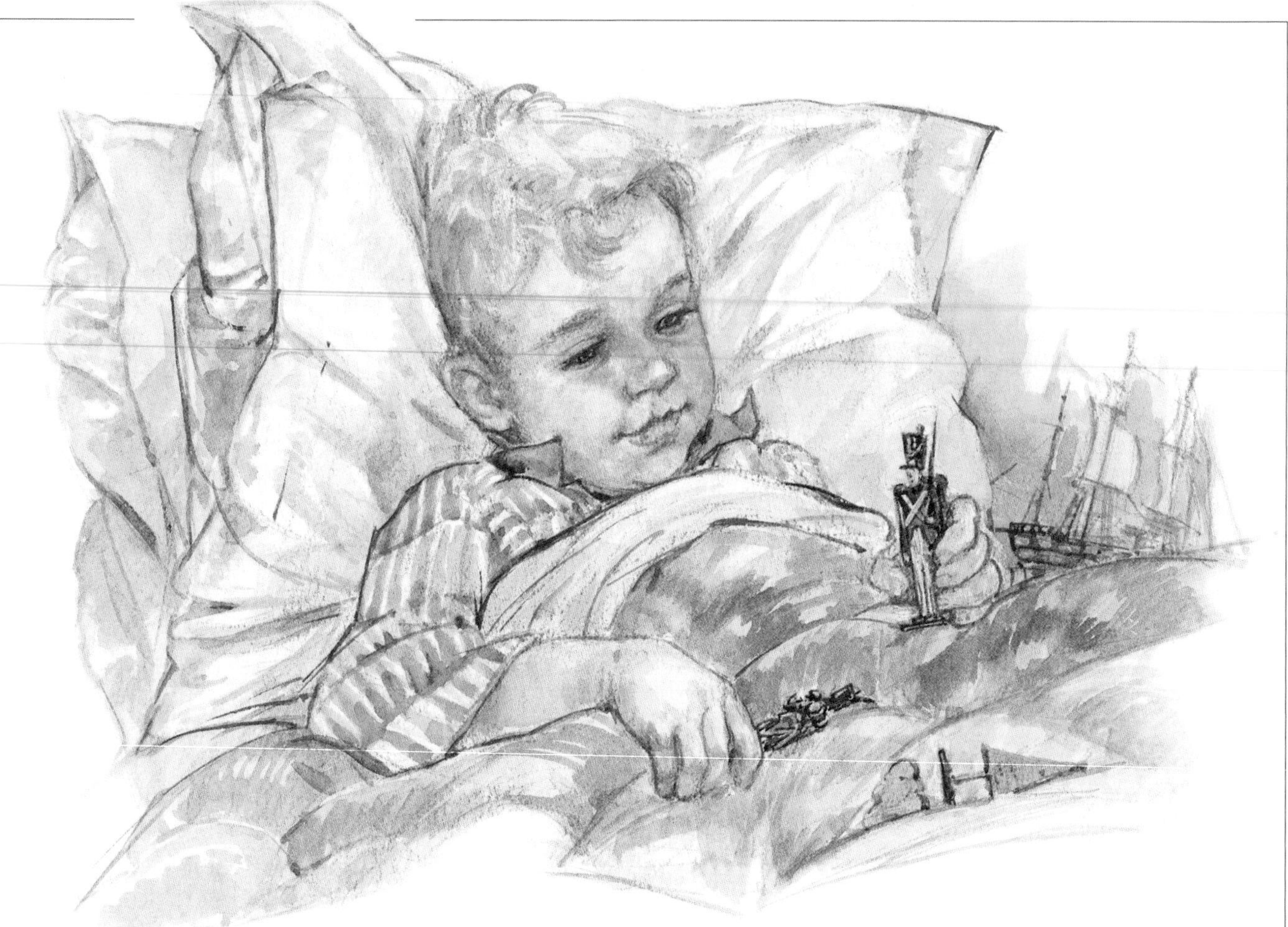

The Land of Counterpane

When I was sick and lay a-bed,
I had two pillows at my head,
And all my toys beside me lay
To keep me happy all the day.

And sometimes for an hour or so
I watched my leaden soldiers go,
With different uniforms and drills,
Among the bed-clothes, through the hills.

And sometimes sent my ships in fleets
All up and down among the sheets;
Or brought my trees and houses out,
And planted cities all about.

I was the giant great and still
That sits upon the pillow-hill,
And sees before him, dale and plain,
The pleasant land of counterpane.

ROBERT LOUIS STEVENSON

Goodnight

Baby, baby, lay your head
   On your pretty cradle bed;
Shut your eye-peeps now the day
   And the light are gone away;
All the clothes are tucked in tight –
   Little baby dear, goodnight.

Yes, my darling, well I know
   How the bitter wind doth blow;
And the winter's snow and rain
   Patter on the window pane;
But they cannot come in here
   To my little baby dear.

For the window shutteth fast
   Till the stormy night is past,
And the curtains warm are spread
   Round about her cradle bed;
So till morning shineth bright,
   Little baby dear, goodnight.

JANE TAYLOR

Sleep, Baby, Sleep

Sleep, baby, sleep!
Your father herds his sheep:
Your mother shakes the little tree
From which fall pretty dreams on thee;
Sleep, baby, sleep!

Sleep, baby, sleep!
The heavens are white with sheep:
For they are lambs, those stars so bright:
And the moon's shepherd of the night;
Sleep, baby, sleep!

Sleep, baby, sleep!
And I'll give thee a sheep,
Which, with its golden bell, shall be
A little play-fellow for thee:
Sleep, baby, sleep!

Sleep, baby, sleep!
And bleat not like a sheep,
Or else the shepherd's angry dog
Will come and bite my naughty rogue;
Sleep, baby, sleep!

Sleep, baby, sleep!
Go out and herd the sheep,
Go out, you barking black dog, go,
And waken not my baby so:
Sleep, baby, sleep!

ANONYMOUS

Young Night Thought

All night long, and every night,
When my mamma puts out the light,
I see the people marching by,
As plain as day, before my eye.

Armies and emperors and kings,
All carrying different kinds of things,
And marching in so grand a way,
You never saw the like by day.

So fine a show was never seen
At the great circus on the green;
For every kind of beast and man
Is marching in that caravan.

At first they move a little slow,
But still the faster on they go,
And still beside them close I keep
Until we reach the town of Sleep.

ROBERT LOUIS STEVENSON

The Land of Nod

From breakfast on all through the day
At home among my friends I stay;
But every night I go abroad
Afar into the land of Nod.

All by myself I have to go,
With none to tell me what to do –
All alone beside the streams
And up the mountainsides of dreams.

The strangest things are there for me,
Both things to eat and things to see,
And many frightening sights abroad
Till morning in the land of Nod.

Try as I like to find the way,
I never can get back by day,
Nor can remember plain and clear
The curious music that I hear.

ROBERT LOUIS STEVENSON

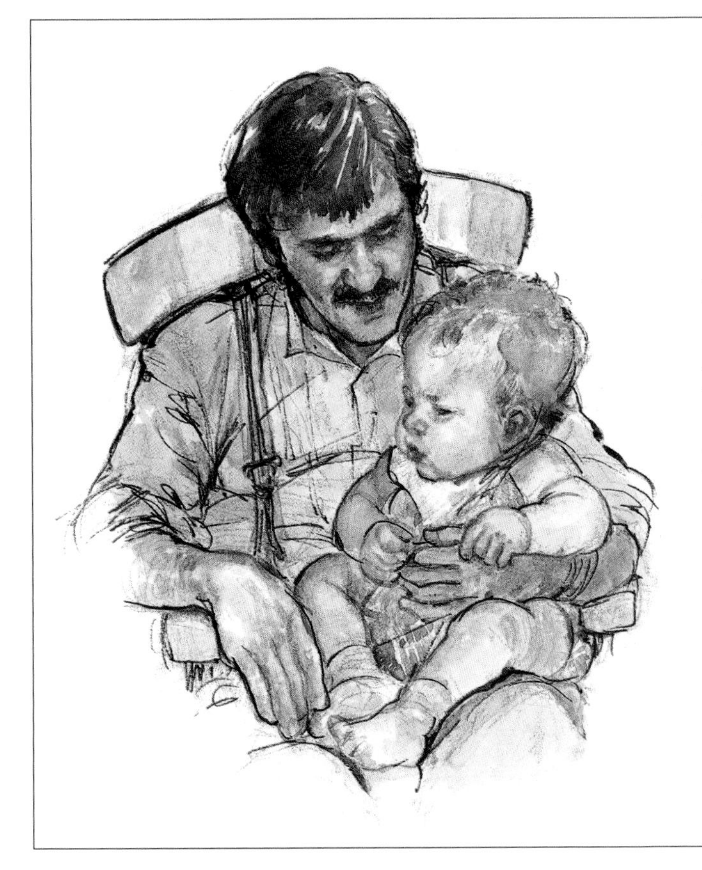

Hush Little Baby

Hush little baby, don't say a word,
Papa's going to buy you a mocking-bird.
If that mocking-bird won't sing,
Papa's going to buy you a diamond ring.
If that diamond ring turns brass,
Papa's going to buy you a looking glass.
If that looking glass gets broke,
Papa's going to buy you a billy goat.
If that billy goat won't pull,
Papa's going to buy you a cart and bull.
If that cart and bull fall down,
You'll still be the sweetest little baby in town.

ANONYMOUS

The Sugar-Plum Tree

Have you ever heard of the Sugar-Plum Tree?
'Tis a marvel of great renown!
It blooms on the shores of the Lollipop Sea
In the garden of Shut-Eye Town;
The fruit that it bears is so wondrously sweet
(As those who have tasted it say)
That good little children have only to eat
Of that fruit to be happy next day.

When you've got to the tree, you would have a hard time
To capture the fruit which I sing;
The tree is so tall that no person could climb
To the bough where the sugar-plums swing!
But up in that tree sits a chocolate cat,
And a gingerbread dog prowls below –
And this is the way you contrive to get at
Those sugar-plums tempting you so.

You say but the word to that gingerbread dog
And he barks with such terrible zest
That the chocolate cat is at once all agog,
As her swelling proportions attest.
And the chocolate cat goes cavorting around
From this leafy limb unto that,
And the sugar-plums tumble, of course, to the ground –
Hurrah for the chocolate cat!

There are marshmallows, gumdrops, and peppermint canes
With stripings of scarlet or gold,
And you carry away of the treasure that rains
As much as your apron can hold!
So come, little child, cuddle closer to me
In your dainty white nightcap and gown,
And I'll rock you away to that Sugar-Plum Tree
In the garden of Shut-Eye-Town.

EUGENE FIELD

The Fly-Away Horse

Oh, a wonderful horse is the Fly-Away Horse,
Perhaps you have seen him before;
Perhaps while you slept his shadow has swept
Through the moonlight that floats on the floor.
For it's only at night, when the stars twinkle bright,
That the Fly-Away Horse, with a neigh
And a pull at his rein and a toss of his mane,
Is up on his heels and away!
The moon in the sky,
As he gallopeth by,
Cries: "Oh, what a marvellous sight!"
And the stars in dismay
Hide their faces away
In the lap of old Grandmother Night.

It is yonder, out yonder, the Fly-Away Horse
Speedeth ever and ever away –
Over meadows and lanes, over mountains and plains,
Over streamlets that sing at their play;
And over the sea like a ghost sweepeth he,
While the ships they go sailing below,
And he speedeth so fast that the men at the mast
Adjudge him some portent of woe,
"What ho there!" they cry
As he flourishes by
With a whisk of his beautiful tail;
And the fish in the sea
Are as scared as can be,
From the nautilus up to the whale!

And the Fly-Away Horse seeks those faraway lands,
You little folk dream of at night –
Where candy-trees grow, and honey brooks flow,
And cornfields with popcorn are white;
And the beasts in the wood are ever so good
To children who visit them there –
What glory astride of a lion to ride,
Or to wrestle around with a bear!
The monkeys, they say:
"Come on, let us play,"
And they frisk in the coconut trees:
While the parrots that cling
To the peanut vines sing
Or converse with comparative ease!

Off! Scamper to bed – you shall ride him tonight,
For, as soon as you've fallen asleep,
With a jubilant neigh he will bear you away
Over forest and hillside and deep!
But tell us, my dear, all you see and you hear
In those beautiful lands over there,
Where the Fly-Away Horse wings his faraway course
With the wee one consigned to his care.
Then Grandma will cry
In amazement: "Oh, my!"
And she'll think it could never be so;
And only we two
Shall know it is true –
You and I, little precious, shall know!

EUGENE FIELD

A Cradle Song

What does the little birdie say
In her nest at peep of day?
Let me fly, says little birdie,
Mother, let me fly away.

Birdie, rest a little longer,
Till the little wings are stronger.
So she rests a little longer
Then she flies away.

What does little baby say
In her bed at peep of day?
Baby says, like little birdie,
Let me rise and fly away.

Baby, sleep a little longer,
Till the little limbs are stronger.
If she sleeps a little longer
Baby, too, shall fly away.

ALFRED, LORD TENNYSON

Dreams

Rose dreamed she was a lily,
Lily dreamed she was a rose;
Robin dreamed he was a sparrow;
What Owl dreamed no one knows.

But they all woke up together
As happy as can be.
Said each: “You’re lovely, neighbour,
But I’m very glad I’m me.”

ANONYMOUS

The Moon

The moon has a face like the clock in the hall;
She shines on thieves on the garden wall,
On streets and fields and harbour quays,
And birdies asleep in the forks of the trees.

The squalling cat and the squeaking mouse,
The howling dog by the door of the house,
The bat that lies in bed at noon,
All love to be out by the light of the moon.

But all of the things that belong to the day
Cuddle to sleep to be out of her way;
And flowers and children close their eyes
Till up in the morning the sun shall rise.

ROBERT LOUIS STEVENSON

Is the Moon Tired?

Is the moon tired? She looks so pale
Within her misty veil;
She scales the sky from east to west,
And takes no rest.

Before the coming of the night
The moon shows papery white;
Before the dawning of the day
She fades away.

CHRISTINA ROSSETTI

The Rock-a-by Lady

The Rock-a-by Lady from Hush-a-by Street
Comes stealing; comes creeping;
The poppies they hang from her head to her feet,
And each hath a dream that is tiny and fleet –
She bringeth her poppies to you, my sweet,
When she findeth you sleeping.

There is one little dream of a beautiful drum –
"Rub-a-dub!" it goeth;
There is one little dream of a big sugar plum,
And lo! thick and fast the other dreams come
Of popguns that bang, and tin tops that hum,
And the trumpet that bloweth.

And dollies peep out of those wee little dreams
With laughter and singing;
And boats go a-floating on silvery streams,
And the stars peek-a-boo with their own misty gleams,
And up, up and up, where Mother Moon beams,
The fairies go winging!

Would you dream all these dreams that are tiny and fleet?
They'll come to you sleeping;
So shut the two eyes that are weary, my sweet,
For the Rock-a-by Lady from Hush-a-by Street,
With poppies that hang from her head to her feet,
Comes stealing, comes creeping.

EUGENE FIELD

PEOPLE and PLACES

Big Greedy Ben

Robin the Bobbin, the Big Greedy Ben,
He ate more meat than four score men;
He ate a cow, he ate a calf,
He ate a butcher–and–a–half;
He ate a church, he ate a steeple,
He ate the priest and all the people!
A cow and a calf,
An ox-and-a-half,
A church and a steeple,
And all the good people,
And yet he complained he was hungry!

ANONYMOUS

Eldorado

Gaily bedight,
  A gallant knight,
In sunshine and in shadow,
  Had journeyed long,
Singing a song,
  In search of Eldorado.

But he grew old –
  This knight so bold –
And o'er his heart a shadow
  Fell, as he found
No spot of ground
  That looked like Eldorado.

And, as his strength
  Failed him at length,
He met a pilgrim shadow
  "Shadow," said he,
"Where can it be –
  This land of Eldorado?"

"Over the Mountains
  Of the Moon,
Down the Valley of the Shadow,
  Ride, boldly ride,"
The shade replied,
  "If you seek for Eldorado!"

EDGAR ALLAN POE

A Tragic Story

There lived a sage in days of yore,
And he a handsome pigtail wore;
But wondered much, and sorrowed more,
Because it hung behind him.

He mused upon this serious case,
And swore he'd change the pigtail's place
And have it hanging at his face,
Not dangling there behind him.

Says he: "The mystery I've found –
I'll turn me round" – he turned around,
But still it hung behind him.

Then round and round, and out and in,
All day the puzzled sage did spin;
In vain – it mattered not a pin –
The pigtail hung behind him.

And right and left, and round about,
And up and down, and in and out,
He turned – but still the pigtail stout
Hung steadily behind him.

And though his efforts never slack,
And though he twist and twirl and tack,
Alas, still faithful to his back,
The pigtail hangs behind him!

OF UNKNOWN GERMAN ORIGIN
(Believed to have been translated by William Thackeray)

The Village Blacksmith

Under a spreading chestnut tree
The village smithy stands;
The smith, a mighty man is he,
With large and sinewy hands;
And the muscles of his brawny arms
Are strong as iron bands.

His hair is crisp, and black, and long,
His face is like the tan;
His brow is wet with honest sweat,
He earns whate'er he can;
And looks the whole world in the face,
For he owes not any man.

Week in, week out, from morn till night,
You can hear his bellows blow;
You can hear him swing his heavy sledge
With measure beat and slow,
Like a sexton ringing the village bell
When the evening sun is low.

And children coming home from school
Look in at the open door;
They love to see the flaming forge
And hear the bellows roar,
And catch the burning sparks that fly
Like chaff from a threshing-floor.

He goes on Sunday to the church,
And sits among his boys;
He hears the parson pray and preach,
He hears his daughter's voice
Singing in the village choir,
And makes his heart rejoice.

It sounds to him like her mother's voice
Singing in Paradise!
He needs must think of her once more
How in the grave she lies,
And with his hard, rough hand he wipes
A tear out of his eyes.

Toiling, rejoicing, sorrowing,
Onward through life he goes;
Each morning sees some task begun,
Each evening sees it close.
Something attempted, something done,
Has earned a night's repose.

Thanks, thanks to thee, my worthy friend
For the lesson though hast taught!
Thus at the flaming forge of Life
Our fortunes must be wrought;
Thus on its sounding anvil shaped
Each burning deed and thought!

HENRY WADSWORTH LONGFELLOW

The Pedlar's Caravan

I wish I lived in a caravan,
With a horse to drive, like a pedlar-man!
Where he comes from nobody knows,
Or where he goes to, but on he goes!

His caravan has windows two,
And a chimney of tin, that the smoke comes through;
He has a wife, with a baby brown,
And they go riding, from town to town.

Chairs to mend and delf to sell!
He clashes the basins like a bell;
Tea-trays, baskets, ranged in order,
Plates with the alphabet round the border!

The roads are brown, and the sea is green,
But his house is just like a bathing machine;
The world is round, and he can ride,
Rumble and splash, to the other side!

With the pedlar-man I should like to roam,
And write a book when I came home;
All the people would read my book,
Just like the Travels of Captain Cook!

WILLIAM BRIGHTY RANDS

Meg Merrilees

Old Meg she was a Gipsy,
And liv'd upon the moors:
Her bed it was the brown heath turf,
And her house was out of doors.

Her apples were swart blackberries,
Her currants pods o' broom:
Her wine was dew o' the wild white rose,
Her book a churchyard tomb.

Her brothers were the craggy hills,
Her sisters larchen trees –
Alone with her great family
She lived as she did please.

No breakfast had she many a morn,
No dinner many a noon,
And 'stead of supper she would stare
Full hard against the moon.

But every morn of woodbine fresh
She made her garlanding,
And every night the dark glen yew
She wove, and she would sing.

And with her fingers old and brown,
She plaited mats o' rushes,
And gave them to the cottagers
She met among the bushes.

Old Meg was brave as Margaret Queen
And tall as Amazon:
An old red blanket cloak she wore;
A chip hat she had on.
God rest her aged bones somewhere –
She died full long agone!

JOHN KEATS

The Windmill

Behold! A giant am I!
 Aloft here in my tower,
With my granite jaws I devour
 The maize, and the wheat and the rye,
And grind them into flour.

I look down over the farms;
 In the fields of grain I see
The harvest that is to be,
 And I fling to the air my arms,
For I know it is all for me.

I hear the sound of flails
 Far off, from the threshing-floors
In barns, with their open doors,
 And the wind, the wind in my sails,
Louder and louder roars.

I stand here in my place,
 With my foot on the rock below,
And whichever way it may blow
 I meet it face to face,
As a brave man meets his foe.

And while we wrestle and strive,
 My master, the miller, stands
And feeds me with his hands;
 For he knows who makes him thrive,
Who makes him lord of lands.

On Sundays I take my rest;
 Churchgoing bells begin
Their low, melodious din;
 I cross my arms on my breast,
And all is peace within.

HENRY WADSWORTH LONGFELLOW

What Bobbie Would Like

I'd like to be a farmer,
With lots of stacks and mows,
And fowl and pigs, and carts and gigs,
And four-and-twenty cows.
I'd drive them all to market
On summer mornings fine;
"Oh, come and buy," I'd stand and cry,
"Buy, buy, good masters mine!"
But if they would not buy them
It would not give me pain.
I'd simply say: "Fair sirs, good-day!"
And drive them home again.

I wish I were a farmer,
With lots of lambs and sheep,
I'd run and play with them all day
Until we went to sleep.
I'd take the wool to market
On summer mornings fine –
"Oh, come and buy," I'd stand and cry,
"Buy, buy, good masters mine!"
But if they would not buy my wool
It would not cause me pain,
I'd come and say: "Dear sheep, good-day,
Here is your wool again."

And if they could not put it on
I'd put it on myself;
And all the rest, when I was dressed,
I'd lay upon the shelf.
For when winter days come round,
And all the world is cold,
I know full well my wool will sell
For all its weight in gold.
And so I'll be a farmer,
Right happy in my lot,
And he who cares may buy my wares,
And other folk need not!

FREDERICK E. WEATHERLY

BRIGHT and BEAUTIFUL

Love Count

One, I love; two, I love;
  Three, I love, I say;
Four, I love with all my heart;
  Five, I cast away;
Six, he loves; seven she loves;
  Eight, both love;
Nine, he comes; ten he tarries;
  Eleven he courts;
And twelve he marries.

ANONYMOUS

Laughing Song

When the green woods laugh with the voice of joy
And the dimpling stream turns laughing by,
When the air does laugh with merry wit,
And the green hill laughs with the noise of it;

When the meadows laugh with lively green,
And the grasshopper laughs in the merry scene;
When Mary, and Susan, and Emily
With their sweet sounding mouths sing, "Ha, ha, he!"

When the painted birds laugh in the shade,
Where our table with cherries and nuts is spread:
Come live, and be merry, and join with me,
To sing the sweet chorus of "Ha, ha, he!"

WILLIAM BLAKE

Autumn Fires

In the other gardens
And all up the vale,
From the autumn bonfires
See the smoke trail!

Pleasant summer over
And all the summer flowers,
The red fire blazes,
The grey smoke towers.

Sing a song of seasons!
Something bright in all!
Flowers in the summer,
Fires in the fall!

ROBERT LOUIS STEVENSON

The Echoing Green

The sun does arise,
And make happy the skies.
The merry bells ring
To welcome the Spring;
The skylark and thrush,
The birds of the bush,
Sing louder around
To the bells' cheerful sound,
While our sports shall be seen
On the Echoing Green.

Old John with white hair,
Does laugh away care,
Sitting under the oak,
Among the old folk.
They laugh at our play,
And soon they shall say:
Such, such were the joys
When we all, girls and boys,
In our youth-time were seen
On the Echoing Green.

Till the little ones, weary,
No more can be merry;
The sun does descend,
And our sports have an end,
Round the laps of their mothers
Many sisters and brothers,
Like birds in their nest,
Are ready for rest,
And sport no more to be seen,
On the darkening Green.

WILLIAM BLAKE

The Flowers

All the names I know from nurse:
Gardener's Garters, Shepherd's Purse,
Batchelor's Buttons, Lady's Smock,
And the Lady Hollyhock.

Fairy places, fairy things,
Fairy woods where the wild bee wings,
Tiny trees for tiny dames –
These must all be fairy names!

Tiny woods below whose boughs
Shady fairies weave a house;
Tiny tree-tops, rose or thyme,
Where the braver fairies climb!

Fair are grown-up people's trees,
But the fairest woods are these;
Where if I were not so tall,
I should live for good and all.

ROBERT LOUIS STEVENSON

Joy of Life

The sun is careering in glory and might
Mid the deep blue sky and the clouds so bright;
The billow is tossing its foam on high,
And the summer breezes go lightly by;
The air and the water dance, glitter and play –
And why should not I be as merry as they?

The linnet is singing the wild wood through,
The fawn's bounding footsteps skim over the dew,
The butterfly flits round the blossoming tree,
And the cowslip and bluebell are bent by the bee:
All the creatures that dwell in the forest are gay,
And why should not I be as merry as they?

MARY RUSSELL MITFORD

WEATHER and SEASONS

Whether The Weather Be Fine

Whether the weather be fine
  Or whether the weather be not,
Whether the weather be cold
  Or whether the weather be hot,
We'll weather the weather
  Whatever the weather,
Whether we like it or not.

ANONYMOUS

The Months

January brings the snow,
Makes your feet and fingers glow.

February brings the rain,
Thaws the frozen lake again.

March brings breezes sharp and chill,
Shakes the dancing daffodil.

April brings the primrose sweet,
Scatters daisies at our feet.

May brings flocks of pretty lambs,
Sporting round their fleecy dams.

June brings tulips, lilies, roses,
Fills the children's hands with posies.

Hot July brings thunder showers,
Apricots and gilly-flowers.

August brings the sheaves of corn;
Then the harvest home is borne.

Warm September brings the fruit;
Sportsmen then begin to shoot.

Brown October brings the pheasant,
Then to gather nuts is pleasant.

Dull November brings the blast –
Hark! The leaves are twirling fast.

Cold December brings the sleet,
Blazing fire and Christmas treat.

SARA COLERIDGE

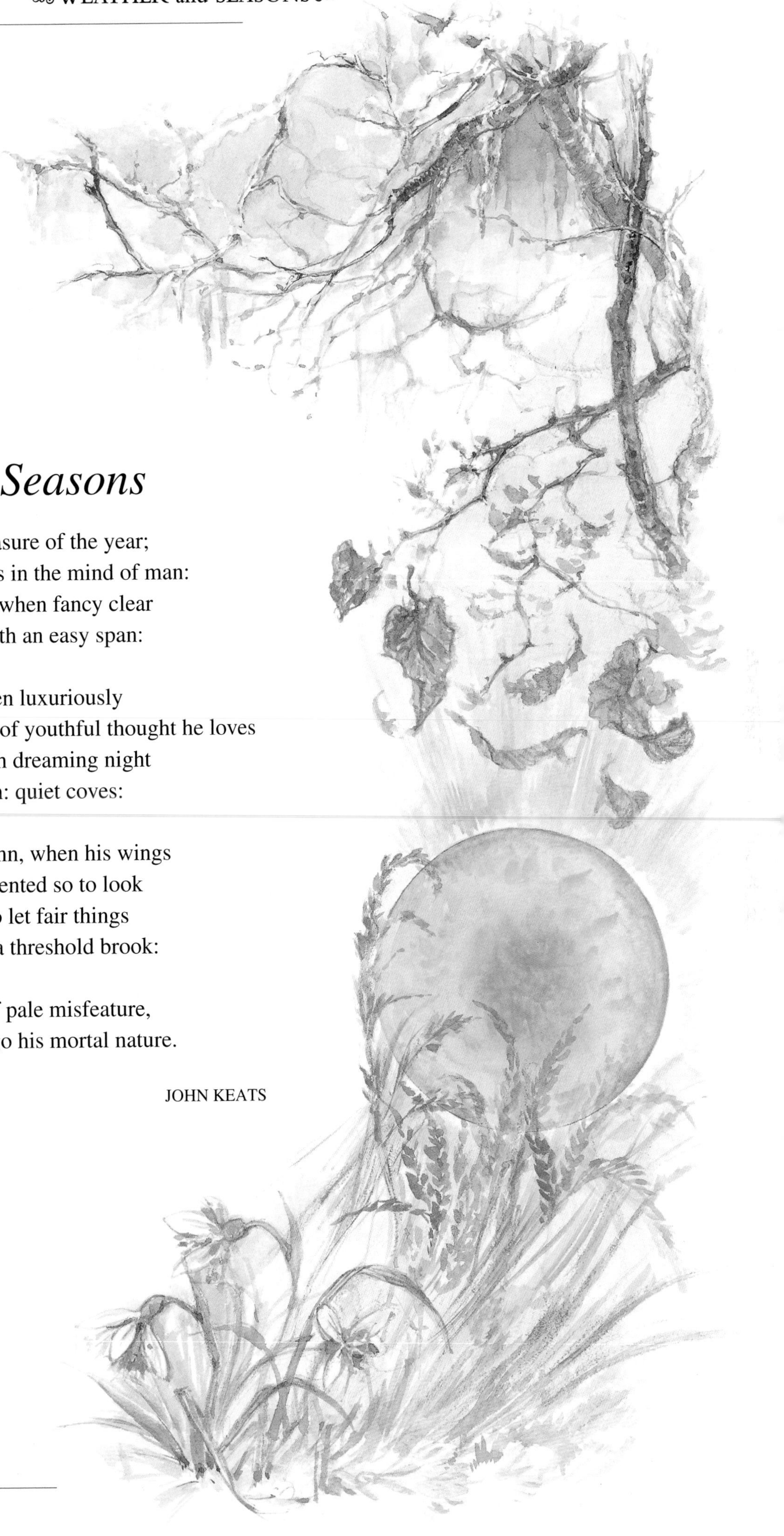

The Human Seasons

Four seasons fill the measure of the year;
There are four seasons in the mind of man:
He has his lusty Spring, when fancy clear
Takes in all beauty with an easy span:

He has his Summer, when luxuriously
Spring's honey'd cud of youthful thought he loves
To ruminate, and by such dreaming night
Is nearest unto heaven: quiet coves:

His soul has in its Autumn, when his wings
He furleth close; contented so to look
On mists in idleness – to let fair things
Pass by unheeded as a threshold brook:

He has his Winter too of pale misfeature,
Or else he would forgo his mortal nature.

JOHN KEATS

The North Wind Doth Blow

The north wind doth blow,
And we shall have snow,
And what will the robin do then,
Poor thing?

He'll sit in a barn,
And keep himself warm,
And hide his head under his wing,
Poor thing.

ANONYMOUS

The Wind

Who has seen the wind?
Neither I nor you;
But when the leaves hang trembling
The wind is passing through.

Who has seen the wind?
Neither you nor I;
But when the trees bow down their heads
The wind is passing by.

CHRISTINA ROSSETTI

The Wind

I saw you toss the kites on high
And blow the birds about the sky;
And all around I heard you pass,
Like ladies' skirts across the grass –
O wind, a-blowing all day long,
O wind, that sings so loud a song!

I saw the different things you did,
But always you yourself you hid.
I felt you push, I heard you call,
I could not see yourself at all –
O wind, a-blowing all day long,
O wind, that sings so loud a song!

O you that are so strong and cold,
O blower, are you young or old?
Are you a beast of field and tree,
Or just a stronger child than me?
O wind, a-blowing all day long,
O wind, that sings so loud a song!

ROBERT LOUIS STEVENSON

Windy Nights

Whenever the moon and stars are set,
Whenever the wind is high,
All night long in the dark and wet,
A man goes riding by.
Late in the night when the fires are out,
Why does he gallop and gallop about?

Whenever the trees are crying aloud,
And ships are tossed at sea,
By, on the highway, low and loud,
By at the gallop goes he.
By at the gallop he goes, and then
By he comes back at the gallop again.

ROBERT LOUIS STEVENSON

The Sound Of The Wind

The wind has such a rainy sound
Moaning through the town,
The sea has such a windy sound –
Will the ships go down?

The apples in the orchard
Tumble from their tree –
Oh, will the ships go down, go down,
In the windy sea?

CHRISTINA ROSSETTI

Spring

Sound the flute!
Now it's mute.
Birds delight
Day and Night;
Nightingale
In the dale,
Lark in Sky,
Merrily,
Merrily, Merrily, to welcome in the Year.

Little Boy,
Full of joy;
Little Girl,
Sweet and small;
Cock does crow,
So do you;
Merry voice,
Infant noise,
Merrily, Merrily, to welcome in the Year.

Little Lamb,
Here I am;
Come and lick
My white neck;
Let me pull
Your soft Wool;
Let me kiss
Your soft face:
Merrily, Merrily, we welcome in the Year.

WILLIAM BLAKE

Rain In Summer

How beautiful is the rain!
After the dust and heat,
In the broad and fiery street,
In the narrow lane,
How beautiful is the rain!

How it clatters along the roofs,
Like the tramp of hoofs!
How it gushes and struggles out
From the throat of the overflowing spout!

Across the window-pane
It pours and pours;
And swift and wide,
With a muddy tide,
Like a river down the gutter roars
The rain, the welcome rain!

HENRY WADSWORTH LONGFELLOW

Fall, Leaves, Fall

Fall, leaves, fall: die, flowers, away;
Lengthen night and shorten day,
Every leaf speaks bliss to me
Fluttering from the autumn tree.

I shall smile when wreaths of snow
Blossom where the rose should grow;
I shall sing when night's decay
Ushers in a drearier day.

EMILY BRONTË

Winter

When icicles hang by the wall,
And Dick the shepherd blows his nail,
And Tom bears logs into the hall,
And milk comes frozen home in pail;

When blood is nipped, and ways be foul,
Then nightly sings the staring owl,
Tu-whit, tu-whoo! A merry note,
While greasy Joan doth keel the pot.

When all aloud the wind doth blow,
And coughing drowns the parson's saw
And birds sit brooding in the snow,
And Marian's nose looks red and raw,

When roasted crabs hiss in the bowl,
Then nightly sings the staring owl.
Tu-whit, tu-whoo! A merry note,
While greasy Joan doth keel the pot.

WILLIAM SHAKESPEARE

Summer Sun

Great is the sun, and wide he goes
Through empty heaven without repose;
And in the blue and glowing days
More thick than rain he showers his rays.

Though closer still the blinds we pull
To keep the shady parlour cool,
Yet he will find a chink or two
To slip his golden fingers through.

The dusty attic, spider-clad,
He, through the keyhole, maketh glad;
And through the broken edge of tiles,
Into the laddered hayloft smiles.

Meantime his golden face around
He bears to all the garden ground,
And sheds a warm and glittering look
Among the ivy's inmost nook.

Above the hills, along the blue,
Round the bright air with footing true,
To please the child, to paint the rose,
The gardener of the World, he goes.

ROBERT LOUIS STEVENSON

LAND and SEA

At The Seaside

When I was down beside the sea
  A wooden spade they gave to me
To dig the sandy shore.
  My holes were empty like an empty cup,
In every hole the sea came up
  Till it could come no more.

ROBERT LOUIS STEVENSON

Where Go The Boats?

Dark brown is the river,
Golden is the sand,
It flows along for ever,
With trees on either hand.

Green leaves a-floating,
Castles of the foam,
Boats of mine a-boating –
Where will all come home?

On goes the river
And out past the mill,
Away down the valley,
Away down the hill.

Away down the river,
A hundred miles or more,
Other little children
Shall bring my boats ashore.

ROBERT LOUIS STEVENSON

Travel

I should like to rise and go
Where the golden apples grow;
Where, below another sky
Parrot islands anchored lie,
And, watched by cockatoos and goats,
Lonely Crusoes building boats;
Where, in sunshine reaching out,
Eastern cities, miles about,
Are with mosque and minaret
Among sandy gardens set,
And the rich goods from near and far
Hang for sale in the bazaar;
Where the Great Wall round China goes,
And on one side the desert blows,
And with bell and voice and drum,
Cities on the other hum;

Where are forests, hot as fire,
Wide as England, tall as a spire,
Full of apes and coco-nuts
And negro hunters' huts;
Where the knotty crocodile
Lies and blinks in the Nile,
And the red flamingo flies
Hunting fish before his eyes;
Where in jungles, near and far,
Man-devouring tigers are,
Lying close and giving ear,
Lest the hunt be drawing near,
Or a comer-by be seen
Swinging in a palanquin;
Where among the desert sands
Some deserted city stands,

All its children, sweep and prince,
Gown to manhood ages since,
Not a foot in street or house,
Not a stir of child or mouse,
And when kindly falls the night,
In all the town no spark of light.
There I'll come when I'm a man
With a camel caravan;
Light a fire in the gloom
Of some dusty dining-room;
See the pictures on the walls,
Heroes, fights and festivals;
And in a corner find the toys
Of the old Egyptian boys.

ROBERT LOUIS STEVENSON

The Captain's Daughter

We were crowded in the cabin –
   Not a soul would dare to sleep –
It was midnight on the waters,
   And a storm was on the deep.

'Tis a fearful thing in winter
   To be shattered by the blast,
And to hear the rattling trumpet
   Thunder: "Cut away the mast!"

So we shuddered there in silence –
   For the stoutest held his breath –
While the hungry sea was roaring
   And the breakers talked with death.

As thus we sat in darkness,
   Each one busy with his prayers,
"We are lost!" the captain shouted,
   As he staggered down the stairs.

But his little daughter whispered,
   As she took his icy hand,
"Isn't God upon the ocean,
   Just the same as on the land?"

Then we kissed the little maiden,
   And we spake in better cheer,
And we anchored safe in harbour
   When the morn was shining clear.

JAMES THOMAS FIELDS

Foreign Lands

Up into the cherry tree
  Who should climb but little me?
I held the trunk with both my hands
  And looked abroad on foreign lands.

I saw the next-door garden lie,
  Adorned with flowers before my eye,
And many pleasant places more
  That I had never seen before.

I saw the dimpling river pass
  And be the sky's blue looking-glass;
The dusty roads go up and down
  With people tramping into town.

If I could find a higher tree
  Farther and farther I should see
To where the grown-up river slips
  Into the sea among the ships.

To where the roads on either hand
  Lead onward into fairy land,
Where all the children dine at five,
  And all the playthings come alive.

ROBERT LOUIS STEVENSON

Pirate Story

Three of us afloat in the meadow by the swing,
  Three of us aboard in the basket on the lea.
Winds are in the air, they are blowing in the spring,
  And waves are on the meadows like the waves there are at sea.

Where shall we adventure, today that we're afloat,
  Wary of the weather and steering by a star?
Shall it be to Africa, a-steering of the boat,
  To Providence, or Babylon, or off to Malabar?

Hi! but here's a squadron a-rowing on to sea –
  Cattle on the meadow a-charging with a roar!
Quick, and we'll escape them, they're as mad as they can be.
  The wicket is the harbour and the garden is the shore.

ROBERT LOUIS STEVENSON

My Ship And I

O it's I that am the captain of a tidy little ship,
Of a ship that goes a-sailing round the pond;
And my ship it keeps a-turning all around and all about;
But when I'm a little older, I shall find the secret out
How to send my vessel sailing on beyond.

For I mean to grow as little as the dolly at the helm,
And the dolly I intend to come alive;
And with him beside to help me, it's a-sailing I shall go,
It's a-sailing on the water, when the jolly breezes blow
And the vessel goes a divie-divie dive.

O it's then you'll see me sailing through the rushes and the reeds,
And you'll hear the water singing at the prow;
For beside the dolly sailor, I'm to voyage and explore,
To land upon the island where no dolly was before,
And to fire the penny cannon in the bow.

ROBERT LOUIS STEVENSON

Where Lies The Land?

Where lies the land to which the ship would go?
  Far, far ahead, is all her seamen know.
And where the land she travels from? Away,
  Far, far behind, is all that they can say.

On sunny moors upon the deck's smooth face,
  Linked arm in arm, how pleasant here to pace;
Or o'er the stern reclining, watch below
  The foaming wake far widening as we go.

On stormy nights when wild north-westers rave,
  How proud a thing to fight with wind and wave!
The dripping sailor on the reeling mast
  Exults to bear, and scorns to wish it past.

Where lies the land to which the ship would go?
  Far, far ahead, is all her seamen know.
And where the land she travels from? Away,
  Far, far behind, is all that they can say.

A.H. CLOUGH

My Kingdom

Down by a shining water well
I found a very little dell,
No higher than my head.
The heather and the gorse about
In summer bloom were coming out,
Some yellow and some red.

I called the little pool a sea;
The little hills were big to me;
For I am very small.
I made a boat, I made a town,
I searched the caverns up and down,
And named them one and all.

And all about was mine, I said,
The little sparrows overhead,
The little minnows too.
This was the world and I was king;
For me the bees came by to sing,
For me the swallows flew.

I played there were no deeper seas,
Nor any wider plains than these,
No other kings than me.
At last I heard my mother call
Out from the house at even-fall,
To call me home to tea.

And I must rise and leave my dell,
And leave my dimpled water well,
And leave my heather blooms.
Alas! and as my home I neared,
How very big my nurse appeared,
How great and cool the rooms!

ROBERT LOUIS STEVENSON

ABOUT the POETS

WILLIAM ALLINGHAM (1824 – 1889)

An Irish poet who often wrote about myths and legends. 'The Fairies' has been a favourite in anthologies since it was first published in 1850. *(Page 26)*

LAURENCE ALMA-TADEMA (1836 – 1912)

The daughter of Sir Lawrence Alma-Tadema, many of Laurence's verses were, in their day, set to music. *(Page 11)*

WILLIAM BLAKE (1757 – 1827)

Born in London, Blake studied at the Royal Academy, illustrating many of his poems with engravings. Began writing verse when aged twelve, but didn't receive full recognition until years after his death. *(Pages 40, 66, 68, 76)*

EMILY BRONTË (1818 – 1848)

The middle of three sisters who all became famous writers – Charlotte (1816 – 1855) and Anne (1820 – 1849). Emily, most famous for her novel 'Wuthering Heights', first published under the name of Ellis Bell. *(Pages 17, 77)*

ARTHUR HUGH CLOUGH (1819 – 1861)

Clough's English father emigrated to the USA during which time son Arthur made many friends, returning to work in England where he developed his poetic skills. *(Page 88)*

THOMAS HARDY (1840 – 1928)

Son of a stonemason, this English novelist and poet was born in Dorset. Articled as an architect at age sixteen, he later worked in London and wrote many novels. Later gave up fiction and devoted himself to preparing his first volume of 'Wessex Poems', published in 1898. *(Page 35)*

ROBERT HERRICK (1591 – 1674)

An English clergyman who, as a poet, drew inspiration for his verses from the lifestyles of ancient Greece and Rome. *(Page 80)*

JAMES HOGG (1770 – 1835)

A Scottish shepherd discovered as a poet by Sir Walter Scott when he submitted his poems for inclusion in an anthology. Hogg then went to Edinburgh where writers such as Byron and Wordsworth became his friends. *(Page 15)*

MARY HOWITT (1799 – 1888)

Born in Coleford, Gloucestershire, the daughter of a prosperous Quaker, Mary went to school in Croydon. Later, she married William Howitt and together they began a career of joint authorship. After settling in Esher, Surrey, in 1833, Mary wrote some verse and tales for children. Among many works she translated from overseas foreign languages were Hans Anderson's fairy tales, published in English under the title of 'Wonderful Stories for Children'. *(Page 37)*

JOHN KEATS (1795 – 1821)

It seemed a cruel twist of fate that having trained originally as a doctor, this gifted poet died of an illness in Rome while still a young man. We must be grateful that he was still able to leave us so many wonderful poems.
(Pages 62, 73)

EDWARD LEAR (1812 – 1888)

Born in London, Lear became a commercial artist when aged fifteen. As a water colour artist he worked for the London Zoological Society as well as being the author of several quite serious books. However, he became best known for his famous 'Book of Nonesense' and his five-line poems known as 'limericks'. *(Page 30)*

HENRY WADSWORTH LONGFELLOW (1807 – 1882)

In between writing epic verse comparable to his 'Hiawatha', Longfellow produced many short poems such as 'The Windmill' and 'Rain in Summer'. *(Pages 60, 63, 76)*

JAMES RUSSELL LOWELL (1819 – 1891)

American poet, born in Massachusettes and educated at Harvard where he succeeded another famous scribe, Henry Wadsworth Longfellow, as Professor of Spanish and English. Also a magazine editor and the U.S.A.'s Minister in Spain (1877 – 80), Lowell wrote several volumes of verse, essays and Civil War memorial odes. *(Page 31)*

MARY RUSSELL MITFORD (1787 – 1855)

Daughter of a Hampshire doctor whose extravagant lifestyle ruined his family, Mary eventually managed to support her father by her earnings as a writer. Rather than a poet, she was better known for her articles in 'The Ladies Magazine' and as a novelist and playwright. *(Page 70)*

EDGAR ALLEN POE (1809 – 1849)

While his spine-chilling horror stories were written for adults, his imaginative poetry has entertained generations of children. *(Page 58)*

WILLIAM BRIGHTY RANDS (1823 – 1882)

Son of a shopkeeper, he began writing as a Parliamentary reporter before becoming one of the best known children's poets of the 19th century. Under several pen-names he also wrote for magazines as well as being the author of books concerned with child morality. (Pages 23, 25, 61)

WILLIAM ROSCOE (1753 – 1831)

William first worked helping his father as a market gardener. He later studied law, then retired from the legal profession to study botany before devoting himself to literature. Apart from poetry, he was the author of works on the Italian Renaissance period, was MP for Liverpool and amassed a fine collection of books and prints. *(Page 28)*

CHRISTINA ROSSETTI (1830 – 1894)

Born in London, the daughter of an Italian exile, Gabriele Rossetti, Christina began writing verse as a child and her first book of poems was published in 1847. More publications followed and by 1866 she had become a beautiful but shy young woman whose fame as a writer was established. *(Pages 33, 42, 55, 74, 75)*

WILLIAM SHAKESPEARE (1564 – 1616)

Shakespeare's poetry, in both plays and sonnets, is considered to be the finest in the English language. Little is known of his early life, but after arriving in London, where he wrote and also acted in most of his plays, his own company started the original Globe Theatre in 1599. *(Pages 32, 77)*

ROBERT LOUIS STEVENSON (1850 – 1894)

Born in Edinburgh, the prolific writer of books, poetry, and essays is buried on top of a mountain near to what had become his home on the South Pacific island of Samoa. There is a fair selection of poems from his famous 'A Child's Garden of Verse' in this book. Poetry apart, his classic novels included 'Kidnapped', 'Treasure Island' and 'A Master of Ballantrae'. More for adults was his famous story of 'Dr. Jekyll and Mr. Hyde'. *(Pages 9, 13, 16, 20, 38, 45, 46, 49, 55, 67, 69, 74, 75, 78, 81, 82, 85, 86, 87, 89 plus inside front cover and inside back cover)*

JANE TAYLOR (1783 – 1824)

Jane Taylor cooperated with sister Ann (1782 – 1866) in many of her published works. Their jointly produced book 'Original Poems for Infant Minds' was published in fifty English editions and translated into Russian, Dutch and German. Their famous 'Twinkle, Twinkle, Little Star' was first published in their 1806 anthology 'Rhymes for the Nursery'. *(Pages 19, 47)*

ALFRED, LORD TENNYSON (1809 – 1892)

Born in Somersby, Lincolnshire, this fine English poet studied at Cambridge University and established himself as a popular writer of his day with such epic and patriotic verse as 'The Charge of the Light Brigade'. As a baron, he entered the House of Lords in 1833 and was appointed Poet Laureate by Queen Victoria in 1850. *(Pages 21, 38, 39, 54)*

FREDERICK E. WEATHERLY (1848 – 1925)

Born in Portshead, Somerset, this barrister was also a writer of many well known songs of the day, with lyrics which transposed easily to verse. 'Muriel and Other Poems' was one of numerous books he wrote specially for children. *(Page 64)*

WILLIAM WORDSWORTH (1770 – 1850)

An English poet who often took his love of Nature as his theme, particularly reflecting his very deep appreciation of the Lake District. *(Pages 22, 41, 42)*

FIRST LINES of VERSES

The Land of Storybooks

At evening when the lamp is lit,
Around the fire my parents sit;
They sit at home and talk and sing,
And do not play at anything.

Now, with my little gun I crawl
All in the dark along the wall,
And follow round the forest track
Away behind the sofa back.

There, in the night, where none can spy,
All in my hunter's camp I lie,
And play at books that I have read,
Till it is time to go to bed.

These are the hills, these are the woods,
These are my starry solitudes;
And there the river by whose brink
The roaring lions come to drink.

I see the others far away
As if in firelight camp they lay,
And I, like to and Indian scout,
About their party prowled about.

So, when nurse comes in for me,
Home I return across the sea,
And go to bed with backward looks
At my dear land of storybooks.

ROBERT LOUIS STEVENSON